FRAMEWORK PROFESSIONAL DEVELOPMENT:

Self-study Modules for Teachers and Lecturers

STRESS MANAGEMENT FOR THE INDIVIDUAL TEACHER

Sandra H. Mills

Framework Press Educational Publishers Ltd.
Parkfield
Greaves Road
LANCASTER
LA1 4TZ

First published 1995

ISBN 1 85008 131 X

**FRAMEWORK PROFESSIONAL DEVELOPMENT:
Self-study Modules for Teachers and Lecturers
STRESS MANAGEMENT FOR THE INDIVIDUAL
TEACHER**

© Sandra H. Mills

The right of Sandra H. Mills to be identified as author of this work
has been asserted by her in accordance with the Copyright,
Designs and Patents Act 1988

A catalogue record for the book is available from the British
Library

All rights reserved

Typeset by Tradespools Ltd., Frome

Printed in Great Britain
by The Charlesworth Group, Huddersfield

Cover design by John Angus
Illustrations by John Fuller

Table of Contents

The Author:

Dr Mills taught for seventeen years in large comprehensive schools. Her Ph.D. thesis investigated the effects of stress on the health and performance of teachers. She is now Managing Director of Stress Management International, a company which trains people in private and public sector organisations to manage stress in the workplace.

Editor:

Karen Westall

Acknowledgements:

The author wishes to thank the following people for their help in the production of this book:

— Jackie Hall for her professional expertise and experience;

— Ann Lawes for ideas and support;

— Doreen Mills for trailing around with administration and for her unending wisdom;

— the numerous individuals who, as educational managers and industrial managers, had such an influence on this book but who must remain nameless.

Introduction

Hello! I am the ghost of Mr Trimble.

I have come to talk to you about a very serious matter: *STRESS*. I wish someone had talked to *me* about it long ago.

No, that's not fair! They did. What I really mean is, I wish I had *listened* to them. But in all fairness, there wasn't the *knowledge* or the *awareness* about stress that there is now.

I want to help you so that you don't end up like me. I destroyed myself but that's not my real regret, you know. No! My *REAL* regret is that I messed everything up for the people and the things that I really *cared* about!

I'm so sorry for the pain I caused my family, friends and work colleagues and all those other people I put through my personal *stress-mangle*.

So, I'm here to make amends by making sure that *YOU* have the opportunity to learn from my mistakes.

Let's start by explaining this journey of personal stress management that I am asking you to embark upon. I'm going to take you through it stage by stage.

This is what it's all about:

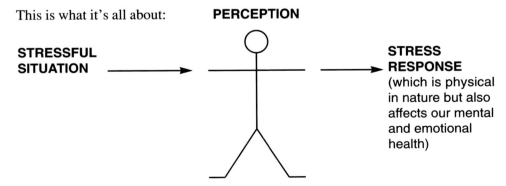

PERCEPTION

STRESSFUL SITUATION

STRESS RESPONSE
(which is physical in nature but also affects our mental and emotional health)

I will be asking you some important questions which you *must* answer truthfully. Completing the activities will help you to achieve the understanding and knowledge to enable you to develop positive and healthy ways of coping with the stress in your life.

I'm going to *TEST* the appropriateness of your attitude to stress in a stressful world and a stressful job.

✤ Get a positive attitude to your stress.

I'm going to *TEACH* you about what stress is; how and why it affects your physical health, your mental abilities, your emotional stability and your behaviour. Hopefully, I'll teach you why you should have a healthy approach.

✤ Understand the stress response.

I'm going to make you *MORE INFORMED* about the physical, mental, emotional and behavioural signs and symptoms of stress that upset our lives and that are usually perceived negatively as 'more problems' rather than positively as 'personal prodders' – as we would use stickers on a 'reminder board'.

✤ Know your warning signs and symptoms of stress.

I'm going to ask you to consider the causal factors of your stress, both at home and at work and then I'm going to tell you that this is all stuff and nonsense and ask you to identify the *REAL* and *PRIMARY* causes of your stress.

✤ Understand the real causes of your stress.

Naturally, I'm going to ask you to consider some tried and tested techniques, devices, strategies for *COPING EFFECTIVELY* and *HEALTHILY* with the stress in your life.

✤ Learn to cope positively with your stress.

At times, I might frighten you a bit. If I do, well I'm sorry, but maybe you *need* to be shaken to make you sit up, think and then move in the right direction!

UNIT 1

What Do You Think about Stress?

I am not a well man. I am suffering from *STRESS*. Everyone knows it because *they too* are suffering because of me. I create problems for colleagues, students, parents, and support staff. But at least they only have to tolerate me at work. My family and friends also suffer because of my stress and, like my colleagues, feel unable to help me.

The situation has not *always* been this way. I was once a fit, well, happy, highly respected and well-liked man. I have steadily progressed to this state, passing through many stages in my slow decline. Along the way, people have tried to help me but have been snubbed and so now they simply avoid me, tolerate me or steadily watch me slide down the slippery slope leading to acute stress-related problems. I am out of touch with myself. I have spent years ignoring the warning signs of stress, which have now resulted in some major problems concerning my physical health (I have a peptic ulcer) and my mental ability (I lose concentration and constantly make mistakes). My behaviour has changed for the worse and everybody at work and at home is affected by it. I flare up at the slightest thing, I slump into depressions, I blame my mistakes on the fact that I am losing sleep, I blame the new legislation for my failure to meet deadlines, I blame everyone for not understanding, I blame management for the bad weather!!!

What are your thoughts at the moment? Keep them in your mind during the following activity.

◆ ACTIVITY 1.1 ◆◆◆

Read my story again and answer the following questions.

Select *three* things that describe the way you feel about Mr Trimble.

1.

2.

3.

How do you think he got into that state?

1.

2.

3.

Suggest *three* pieces of advice for Mr Trimble.

1.

2.

3.

State *three* things that you believe will ensure you are not, and never will be, like Mr Trimble. (The first item is completed for you!)

1. I am reading this book and intend to learn from it!

2.

3.

How do you think other people would answer the previous question for you?

1. My family would say:

2. My colleagues would say:

UNIT 2

Understanding Stress

Stress is obviously a potential enemy to your physical and mental well-being and hence to your *PERFORMANCE*. To *ensure* that you avoid *my* fate, you need to know what you are up against.

◆ **ACTIVITY 2.1** ◆◆◆

In order to clarify the way you approach your stress at the moment, record your responses to the following issues, stating the reasons for those responses and then compare them with the reasons offered at the end of the activity.

Issue	Yes/No	Why?
1. I should fear stress.		
2. I should respect stress.		
3. I should endure stress.		
4. I should succumb to stress.		

Allowing for terminology, your answers should have been as follows:

1. Yes. It can destroy me, my home life and my working life *if I let it*!

2. Yes. It is a formidable force and an opponent in my quest for a *healthy and happy life*.

3. Yes and no. YES, when stressful and unavoidable life events such as bereavement occur. Otherwise, NO.

4. Never. Even when confronted with No. 3, there is always *something* to gain, *something* to learn and *something* to take with you as a strengthener to life's problems.

Are we saying that stress is always:

— a scourge?
— a problem?
— negative?
— unhealthy?

If we do, we are wrong. Stress is indeed a formidable force. It *can* destroy us but only if we allow it to do so.

You *can* manage it. You *can* control it in most circumstances and you *can* use it for your personal benefit. *Everyone* has experienced at least one situation when stress has given them the following:

- More energy
- More concentration
- More creativity
- More positive attitudes

- More enthusiasm
- More self-belief
- More determination

◆ ACTIVITY 2.2 ◆◆◆

Consider this *positive* side of stress and recall *three* occasions when the stress you were under actually *helped* you.

1.

2.	
3.	

❖

In the stress clinic we have here, there are some 'Did you know?' posters dotted about. Naturally, I hadn't known anything!

◆ ACTIVITY 2.3 ◆◆◆

How many of these bits of information about stress do you already know? Tick items that you are already aware of and place a cross against details that are new to you.

✤ There are two types of stress: one is positive and good for me, the other is negative and bad for me.

✤ Stress-related illness originates from the STRESS RESPONSE which is physical in nature and is activated in my *body* when my *mind* detects a threat, or a challenge, or indeed any situation that requires a boost of energy.

✤ 85% of all illness is considered to be stress-related.

✤ Stress costs this country billions of pounds per year through absenteeism (from stress-related illness and inappropriate coping devices such as alcohol and drug abuse), mistakes, accidents, disputes and the reduced performance of people in the workplace.

✤ Some insurance companies are refusing to insure organisations for claims unless they can prove that they have an active stress management policy for their workforce.

✤ The stress response in my body is activated *solely* by *me*! Nothing or no one can activate it for me.

✚ Stress-related illness occurs as a result of the *cumulative* effects of activating my stress response.

How well informed are you?
What new pieces of information are you surprised by and why?
Will any of these pieces of information influence your future approach to the stress in your life? If so, how?

❖

I need to tell you about a basic principle of stress so look at the diagram I've drawn for you.

The Stress/Performance Curve

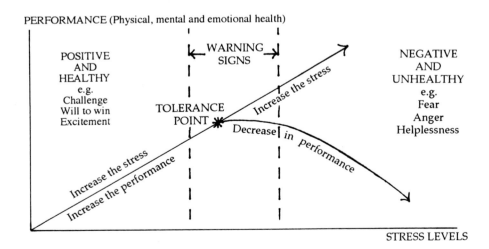

PERFORMANCE (Physical, mental and emotional health)

POSITIVE AND HEALTHY
e.g.
Challenge
Will to win
Excitement

WARNING SIGNS

Increase the stress

NEGATIVE AND UNHEALTHY
e.g.
Fear
Anger
Helplessness

TOLERANCE POINT

Decrease in performance

Increase the stress
Increase the performance

STRESS LEVELS

The *straight line* represents the amount of STRESS you are feeling. Don't confuse this with the amount of WORK you do.

The *curved line* represents your PERFORMANCE, which reflects your physical health, mental ability, emotional stability and your behaviour.

The two lines run together on the left-hand side of the diagram. This is because the left-hand side of the curve is positive and healthy: here you are using the stress response to give you energy, more concentration and greater brainpower. You *feel* challenged and you *achieve* success for your efforts.

Look at where the two lines separate. This is your TOLERANCE POINT and you *must* be able to recognise when you have reached it. If you don't, you move into the right-hand side of the diagram where you *feel* under threat, afraid, frustrated or annoyed. In this state, your health and well-being will deteriorate, as mine did! I ignored the warning signs that appear around the tolerance point and look what happened to me!

◆ ACTIVITY 2.4 ◆◆◆

On the Stress/Performance Curve below, place a cross where you feel you are *now* and then answer the attached questions.

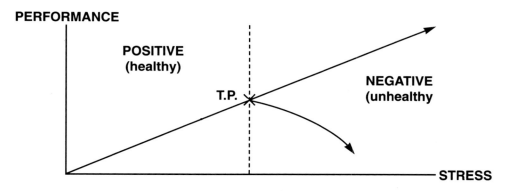

PERFORMANCE

POSITIVE
(healthy)

T.P.

NEGATIVE
(unhealthy

STRESS

Why have you placed your cross here?

How does it make you *feel*?
If your cross is on the RIGHT, how do you cope? What do you do to make yourself feel better?
In what situations would your cross have been on the LEFT?
Consider the ways in which you cope with negative stress generally. Do they work? Explain your answer.

I've been mentioning this STRESS RESPONSE quite a lot and so I think I'd better check that you understand what it is. Then you'll see why it's so important. If only I'd *known* what I was doing to myself every time I got angry, upset or frustrated, I would have taken more control over my emotions and the things that caused these feelings.

But would I?

A man's just moved in here. Last week, in fact. Do you know, his employer had provided STRESS MANAGEMENT and TIME MANAGEMENT training courses but he *still* ended up with a heart attack! When he was tackled about it, he said 'I didn't think it applied to me. I thought stress only affected weaklings!'

What an idiot!

Anyway, back to the STRESS RESPONSE and how some knowledge about it can help you to live a healthier, happier and, with luck, a longer life.

◆ ACTIVITY 2.5 ◆◆◆

Tick items listed below that you already know. Circle any items that you didn't know and remember them in the future when you start to get angry, frustrated, upset, etc.

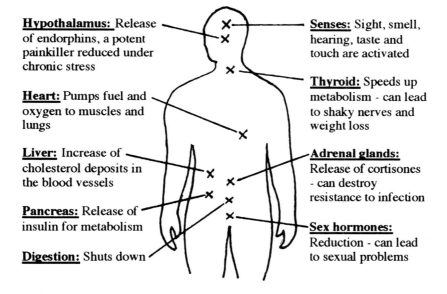

Hypothalamus: Release of endorphins, a potent painkiller reduced under chronic stress

Heart: Pumps fuel and oxygen to muscles and lungs

Liver: Increase of cholesterol deposits in the blood vessels

Pancreas: Release of insulin for metabolism

Digestion: Shuts down

Senses: Sight, smell, hearing, taste and touch are activated

Thyroid: Speeds up metabolism - can lead to shaky nerves and weight loss

Adrenal glands: Release of cortisones - can destroy resistance to infection

Sex hormones: Reduction - can lead to sexual problems

Are you pleased with your existing knowledge?
What information have you learned in this activity?

> What aspects of the STRESS RESPONSE have had the greatest impact on you?

There are some major learning points here for us. After all, if stress-related illness is what we want to protect ourselves from, the simple answer must be to:

KEEP PHYSICALLY FIT	ENSURE A GOOD DIET

ELIMINATE ALL NEGATIVE EMOTIONS	AVOID ALL SITUATIONS AND PEOPLE THAT MIGHT ACTIVATE A STRESS RESPONSE

Nice, if you can guarantee it! But life and people are not so easily controlled, are they? You DO get angry, you DO get frustrated and life DOES go against you at times. Because of this, you've got to develop a sensible, realistic and balanced approach to the stress in your life. There's no doubt that exercise, the burning off of 'stress products' in the body, plays a major role in stress management. I was a couch potato! And yes, I'll readily admit that my diet was very suspect and contributed to my demise, but when they examined me here, they found that my arteries were blocked up mainly with chemicals released through stress.

They said that I'd selected the wrong ways to cope with the stress in my life, so later in this book, I'm going to show you the NEGATIVE and UNHEALTHY coping devices that I chose and then show you the coping devices I *should* have selected. But for now, while I'm still getting you to *understand* stress, I'm going to show you how the whole process of stress and coping works.

◆ **ACTIVITY 2.6** ◆◆◆

Look at the following diagram and answer the questions below according to what you do *now*.

The Process of Stress

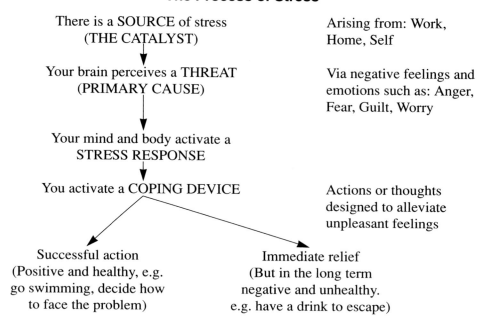

There is a SOURCE of stress
(THE CATALYST)

Arising from: Work, Home, Self

Your brain perceives a THREAT
(PRIMARY CAUSE)

Via negative feelings and emotions such as: Anger, Fear, Guilt, Worry

Your mind and body activate a
STRESS RESPONSE

You activate a COPING DEVICE

Actions or thoughts designed to alleviate unpleasant feelings

Successful action
(Positive and healthy, e.g.
go swimming, decide how
to face the problem)

Immediate relief
(But in the long term
negative and unhealthy.
e.g. have a drink to escape)

What NEGATIVE and UNHEALTHY coping devices do you *know* you use at times when you feel under stress?

What POSITIVE and HEALTHY coping devices do you *think* you use at times when you feel under stress?

Are you able to recognise your TOLERANCE POINT and hence the need to activate positive and healthy coping devices?

One thing they do with you when you get here is a LIFE ANALYSIS. They show you what you've done well and what you've done wrong. I want to check that everything so far has been clear and that you understand the major points I've been trying to make.

◆ ACTIVITY 2.7 ◆◆◆

Listed below are the major points I've made. Read them and tick them if you're happy that the message has sunk in.

If you're not happy with your level of knowledge, go back and read the appropriate parts again.

✤ Stress does not just affect weaklings. All human beings experience stress. □

✤ Stress is to be feared, respected and sometimes endured but I should never succumb to it and become a victim of it. □

✤ Most stress that I face *can* be dealt with as long as I have a positive attitude towards it. □

✤ When I am experiencing emotions such as challenge, achievement, pride and determination, I am using stress positively and it is good for me. □

✤ When I am experiencing negative emotions such as anger, fear, helplessness and worry, I am on the right-hand side of the Stress/Performance Curve and therefore doing myself harm. □

✤ My Tolerance Point is the point at which my positive and healthy emotions switch to negative and unhealthy feelings and this tolerance point tells me that I am moving into the danger zone. □

✤ I move back from negative stress to positive stress by using coping devices. □

✤ There are two types of coping devices: those that are positive and healthy and those that are negative and unhealthy. □

UNIT 3
The Signs and Symptoms of Stress

Look back to the diagram on p. 8 for a minute because I want to say a bit more about your tolerance point. You're fortunate here because your mind and body give you warnings that things are not right. These warning signs are mild at first, but if they do not succeed in making you 'take action', they will become more severe.

I had dozens of warning signs such as headaches, constant colds and other minor infections, sleep disturbances and outbursts of temper. But I ignored them, so they became worse. I then experienced stomach acidity, bilious attacks, recurring throat infections and my headaches became more migrainous in description. I also started making silly mistakes, became uncommonly forgetful and then my errors started to affect other people.

Rather than ACKNOWLEDGING these unpleasant phenomena as 'messages from my brain', I chose the easy option and buried my head in the sand: enduring them, explaining them, justifying them and making silly excuses for them to myself and to those around me.

In *Activity 1.1*, you probably described me as an *idiot* to allow the situation to become so bad, and yet spare a thought for me, because I am so typical of people who ignore simple warning signs. Wrapped up in the pressures and demands placed upon us, we relegate our own well-being to a position of low priority.

It's true, isn't it? I mean, if you had a beacon fitted to the end of your nose that lit up when you approached your tolerance point, you would take notice. You would know that everyone else could see it and you would *DO SOMETHING* about it.

Do you know what all *your* warning signs are? I bet you don't. I bet you know *some* of them. But, from experience, I can tell you that you're perceiving some vital warning signs as totally unrelated to stress.

I argued that my bed was to blame for my sleep disturbances! They said it was the result of my stress response still being switched on even though I was asleep.

They said I'd failed to identify careless mistakes as a warning sign. I said, 'Well, of *course* I made mistakes. I was tired because I hadn't slept well because my bed was uncomfortable!'

Then they showed me deep into the workings of my mind and my body and it all became clear.

I can't take you deep into *your* mind and body but I can draw your attention to what I *know now* and wish I'd known then.

◆ ACTIVITY 3.1 ◆◆◆

Look more closely at your personal signs and symptoms of stress and complete the following:

Name *six* things that happen to you PHYSICALLY when you are under stress.
Name *six* things that happen to you MENTALLY and EMOTIONALLY when you are under stress.
Name *six* things that happen to your BEHAVIOUR when you are under stress.

In terms of self-knowledge, rate yourself by circling one of the following numbers for each statement.

0...Very poor   3...Good
1...Not too good   4...Very good
2...Satisfactory   5...Excellent

I know my PHYSICAL warning signs of stress, watch for them and take note of them.	0 1 2 3 4 5
I know my MENTAL and EMOTIONAL warning signs of stress, watch for them and take note of them.	0 1 2 3 4 5
I know my BEHAVIOURAL warning signs of stress, watch for them and take note of them.	0 1 2 3 4 5
I can recognise the warning signs of stress in my family.	0 1 2 3 4 5
I can recognise the warning signs of stress in my colleagues.	0 1 2 3 4 5

Even if your scores suggest a level of knowledge above the average, you should still participate in the activities offered in the remainder of this section. As you've probably guessed, I've now been shown that the WARNING SIGNS and SYMPTOMS of stress fall into three major categories:

❖ Your PHYSICAL signs and symptoms: anything that happens to your *body* as a result of stress

❖ Your MENTAL and EMOTIONAL signs and symptoms: anything relating to your ability to use your brain and anything relating to the way you *feel* emotionally, inside

❖ Your BEHAVIOURAL signs and symptoms: anything relating to the way you conduct yourself: what you do, how you do it; what you say, how you say it

I am going to present you with the most common physical, mental/emotional and behavioural warning signs of stress and ask you to identify any that you experience, but, because it can come as a bit of a shock, I'm going to ease you into it by having a bit of fun first. My life analysis showed that I didn't have enough fun, taking everything too seriously. In fact, my appraisal concluded that I had been: 'An obsessive personality, perceiving minor, average and semi-major obstacles as persistently insoluble, resulting in an ongoing intense dwelling and inability to life-prioritise.' Basically, I was boring. So have fun doing the next activity.

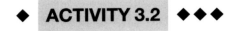

◆ ACTIVITY 3.2 ◆◆◆

Tick the appropriate box if you recognise in yourself any of the following teaching ailments:

Friday Night Fever   ☐

Symptoms: Exhaustion and lethargy as the relief of another week completed hits the already over-tired anatomy. Lounging on settee seen as a waste of time, leading to feelings of guilt. Tendency to increase alcohol intake as a hang-over the next morning will not disrupt work capacity.

Sunday Tea-time Twinge   ☐

Symptoms: Lowering of energy levels as Monday morning grows closer. Resentment at having to rush work planned for the previous Friday evening. Edginess and grumpiness as the next weekend appears so far away.

First Week of a Holiday Malaise   ☐

Symptoms: Inability to do all the things you planned, because of exhaustion, colds, coughs, flu and stomach bugs requiring bed-rest for two or three days. Feelings of injustice at being ill during a holiday.

The Night before 5G Cramps   ☐

Symptoms: Anticipation that the following day will be unpleasant with difficult classes, duties, deadlines and no free lessons. Accompanied by headaches and being edgy with spouse, children or inanimate objects. Craving for sweet or spicy foods to brace the body for the onslaught. Possible difficulties with sleep or sexual experiences.

First Week Back Slumps   ☐

Symptoms: Distinct absence of enthusiasm and commitment, accompanied by sighs, clock-watching and wistful memories of the non-stressful holiday. Constant need to chatter to offset realisation of returning to pressure zone. A decidedly 'unwell' feeling and trauma.

Presenteeism   ☐

Symptoms: Fear of being absent, although totally unfit for work. Reluctance to place added strain on colleagues and pupils. Pathetic attempts to cope with illness exacerbate the situation. The dangerously high levels of potions and pills swirling around the body cause nausea and fatigue. Longing for time to go home and sleep. Increased sensitivity to noise, especially from pupils and school bells.

Absentee Guilt Syndrome

Symptoms: Inability to relax and get on with the job of being poorly. Guilt at pressure imposed on colleagues and pupils. Determination to return to school as soon as legs will carry body weight. Internal conflict between debt to school and attention to the needs of the only body you will ever have.

Classroomia Nervosa

Symptoms: Distancing of mind from surroundings at school. Wistful sighs, vacant expressions, thoughts of jobs to be done at home as the mind attempts to extricate itself from being somewhere it does not want to be. Associated with too much paperwork and poor behaviour of children. Recently linked to feelings of diminished status, poor pay and lack of power to control the direction of the profession. 'Cotton wool head' often transcends the immediate problem and permits survival but is damaging in the long term.

Martyrdom's Revenge

Symptoms: Decline in the desire to uphold excellent records of attendance and efficiency, when totally unfit for the demanding work and with no time in which to do it. Afflicts the long-serving teacher who no longer feels that neglect of health is appreciated or sensible. Typical manifestations include migraine, flu, acute digestive disorders, nervous complaints and backache requiring bed-rest or long-term absence from school.

Good Will Gangrene

Symptoms: Arising from years of accepting enforced legislation, change and upheaval. Reduced morale and little motivation to do extra work without extra pay or extra time. Lethargic and suspicious reception of new ideas. Dismay at re-inventing the wheel and disdain towards new jargon, disguising what you have been doing for years. This ailment is now rampant in the teaching profession, causing conflict between staff and management who know that much of the climate of the school relies heavily on good will.

How much TRUTH is there in the imaginary ailments mentioned above?

How often do you hear other teachers, unwittingly, refer to these ailments?

Being serious now, let's *really* identify the signs that you are approaching, or have reached *or even gone beyond*, your tolerance point.

Let me explain, because this is *exactly* what happened to me. When I was at my tolerance point, my mind and body put Plan A into action. I experienced some minor warning signs in the form of reflux (I kept feeling acid coming up in my throat), sleep disturbances (I kept waking up at exactly 3.27 a.m.) and I was losing my ability to concentrate at work, leading to mistakes, forgetfulness and failure to meet important deadlines.

But what did I do? I made excuses for all these symptoms. I blamed the food, the bed, other people, the system and, above all, the workload.

So I ignored the warning signs. In my life analysis, it was made clear to me how my mind and body dealt with my refusal to be warned.

My mind said, 'What's the matter with you, Trimble? Why aren't you listening to the warnings I'm giving you? Not *loud enough* for you, eh? O.K., then I'll employ Plan B. That should make you take notice.' So my mind told my body to put the frighteners on me. I got awful stomach problems. My doctor tired of seeing me when one viral infection followed another.

I let people down, my desk became known as the BERMUDA RECTANGLE because I kept losing important messages and papers. I went into temper tantrums and created conflict with colleagues. The students suffered at the end of my tongue and I found myself getting into situations that I later regretted.

Meanwhile, I dumped all this stress on my family and friends. But I still didn't accept that my mind and body were sending clear messages of warning to me and I *still* insisted on blaming everything and everyone for these problems.

Finally, my mind and body got together for a crisis summit meeting and decided that I was so far down the right-hand side of the Stress/Performance Curve that only Plan C could salvage the situation.

Plan C proved to be very unpleasant but by now I had lost my ability to reason and think rationally. What *didn't* they throw at me? My stomach problems turned into an ulcer. I woke up in the night with chest pains, sweating and convinced I was having a heart attack. I had every medical test available to mankind and became obsessed with illness. I became immune to criticism and found it easy to isolate myself and withdraw from hobbies and activities that I had once enjoyed. I picked arguments wherever possible because this released my tension and I became intolerant of people who could not appreciate the enormous stress I was under.

Plan C did not work.

I'm sorry, mind. I'm sorry, body.

I'm sorry, family friends, colleagues and students.

Oh, I wish I could do it all over again. I'd complete the next three activities and really take note of them.

◆ ACTIVITY 3.3 ◆◆◆

Put a tick in the box beside any of the following physical signs and symptoms of stress that you experience.

Frequent headaches		Head noises, ringing in ears	
Heart palpitations		Butterflies in stomach	
Loud, thumping heart during night		Heartburn, indigestion, stomach cramps, acidic problems	
Reflux		Irritable bowel syndrome	
Chest pains		Throat infections	
Lumps in throat, difficulty swallowing		Psoriasis, shingles, eczema, rosacea	
Becoming full of gas, feeling uncomfortable later in day		Tense facial muscles especially round eyes and mouth	
Trembling hands		Viral infections	
Constant colds and other minor infections		Muscular pains especially in back, shoulders and neck	
Skin irritations, rashes, blemishes		Feeling light headed, fearing you will faint	

Dry mouth		Visiting toilet frequently	
Sickly feelings		Sore or infected eyes	
Sore or infected ears		Allergies	
Sweating for no obvious reason		Noticing more illness in your life these days	
Bladder or bowel infections			

Record here your *six* most frequent physical signs of stress.

How do they compare with your answers in *Activity 3.1*?

◆ ACTIVITY 3.4 ◆◆◆

Now put a tick in the box beside any of these mental and emotional signs of stress you have noticed in yourself.

Losing interest in paperwork		Being easily distracted	
Getting upset quickly or taking offence easily		Losing interest in teaching, preparation or marking	
Waking up early, suddenly, with things on your mind		Day-dreaming, staring into space, fantasising	
Making mistakes more often		Becoming forgetful	
Finding it hard to make decisions		Dwelling heavily on problems and incidents	

Becoming clumsy		Being unable to relax	
Losing your sense of humour		Feeling trapped	
Losing concentration quickly in class or in a meeting		Laughing and joking less frequently, becoming intense	
Dreading the future		Over-reacting	
Feeling out of control of situations or life in general		Experiencing a recurrent fear of disease	
Feeling helpless, persecuted, resenting your situation and experiencing hopelessness		Feeling that you are biding time, treading water and waiting for something nice to happen	
Enjoying arguments and conflicts		Being suspicious of people's motives	
Feeling tearful, dull, less 'on the ball', less enthusiastic		Giving up on yourself, your situation and other people	
Regretting your actions, words and behaviour in general		Feeling uglier, fatter, less competent – poor self-esteem	
Becoming stubborn and less helpful		Becoming lethargic or easily bored	
Looking for arguments			

What are your *six* main warning signs in this category?

How do they compare with your answers in *Activity 3.1*?

◆ ACTIVITY 3.5 ◆◆◆

Again, put a tick in the box against those behavioural symptoms you notice in yourself. After completing the activity, ask other people (at work and at home) to complete it according to their perceptions of you. Then compare the responses!

I interrupt others when they are speaking		I become obsessive about minor issues	
I become sarcastic or flippant		I put things off	
I become impatient and fly off the handle		I experience and express acute swings of moods	
I develop a nervous laugh		I cry easily	
I become moody		I fidget	
I smoke more		I drink more alcohol	
I eat more		I eat less	
I turn to sweet, spicy or convenience foods		I allow work to take precedence over home, family, friends	
I become isolated and distant		I talk, eat or walk faster	
I sigh a lot		I develop tics and habits	
I make irrational decisions		I take more time off work	
I avoid doing the hard but really important jobs		I upset people	

What are your *six* main warning signs in this category?

How do they compare with your answers in *Activity 3.1*?

Before moving on, check that you have understood all the learning points from this unit and say to yourself, 'I am going to take heed of all my warning signs and I will ask family, friends and colleagues to tell me when *they* spot the signs.'

UNIT 4
The Causal Factors of Stress

Do you know what really used to 'get' me?...Wednesdays!

I was on duty *FIVE* times that day *and* I had no free periods *and* I had to face two of my worst classes. Oh, how I hated Wednesdays. I was a 'victim' of Wednesdays and succumbed to what I thought was the inevitable. I was dreading Wednesday even on Monday and I was still angry about it on Friday!

One really important thing about the causes of stress that I've learned is that most of our stress is created by ourselves. Crazy, isn't it? That's *just* what I said to them.

I said straight out, 'Look, when you're faced with a 15 year-old swearing at you and humiliating you when you're exhausted and you know nothing will be done about him, THAT'S STRESSFUL! They smiled politely and replied, 'Only because you let it be.'

What they were getting me to understand was the difference between CATALYSTS and PRIMARY CAUSES of stress. For me, the CATALYSTS had been the long day, the duties and the rude boy but the PRIMARY CAUSES of my stress had been anger (at the boy), frustration (about the duties), and the loss of control (of my day).

Remember when I showed you the stress response and we decided that stress management was finding ways of controlling it so it didn't do us harm? Well, rude pupils, duties and mountains of paperwork (catalysts) cannot switch that stress response on. It can only be activated by YOU via the negative emotions you are experiencing.

◆ ACTIVITY 4.1 ◆◆◆

Consider the following emotions and organise them into the two categories listed below.

Success   Failure   Achievement   Guilt

Anger	Anxiety	Contentment	Despair
Triumph	Loss	Exhilaration	Pride
Challenge	Insecurity	Remorse	Disappointment
Elation	Inadequacy	Helplessness	Grief
Hopelessness	Annoyance	Satisfaction	Determination
Frustration	Fear of failure		

Category 1 – Pleasant feelings	*Category 2 – Unpleasant feelings*
e.g. Success	e.g. Failure
Which category do *you* experience the most?	
What *three* emotions in *Category 2* do you experience the most?	

Now let's make sure that you can differentiate between your catalysts and your primary causes. We're going to do this by separating work from home.

◆ ACTIVITY 4.2 ◆◆◆

Use your results from *Activity 4.1* to complete the following table. Against each CATALYST, state what you think is the PRIMARY CAUSE of this state. In the first three, you are given three choices and, although all three may apply, ONE is the REAL primary cause for you. Tick the one you feel is correct. For the next three, select your own primary cause for each catalyst and for the final two, select both catalyst and primary cause.

Catalyst	Primary cause
Unrealistic deadlines	a) Anger b) Fear of failure c) Anxiety
What is the reason for your choice of answer?	
Too much administration, too little teaching	a) Disappointment b) Guilt c) Frustration
What is the reason for your choice of answer?	
Unruly and disruptive pupils	a) Annoyance b) Helplessness c) Remorse
What is the reason for your choice of answer?	
Problems with colleagues	
What is the reason for your choice of PRIMARY CAUSE?	
Problems with higher management	
What is the reason for your choice of PRIMARY CAUSE?	
Anticipation of future situation	

What is the reason for your choice of PRIMARY CAUSE?	
What is the reason for your choice of PRIMARY CAUSE?	
What is the reason for your choice of PRIMARY CAUSE?	

It would be nice to think that NEGATIVE and UNHEALTHY STRESS existed solely within the confines of the working world. We could then gear ourselves to what could be perceived as a *temporary* and *short-lasting* onslaught.

I'm sure you're like I was: experiencing problems in my home and social life as well as those at work. Mind you, I must admit now, looking back, that many of my problems at home were probably because I allowed work to invade my home.

◆ **ACTIVITY 4.3** ◆◆◆

Applying what you have learned about catalysts and primary causes from *Activities 4.1* and *4.2*, complete the chart. There are spaces for you to add your own category.

Category	What happens? (Catalyst)	How does this make you feel? (Primary Cause)
Relationship with partner		

Relationship with children		
Relationship with wider family		
Relationship with friends		
The home: size, area, condition, etc.		
Financial status		
Relationship with neighbours		

Adding together the amounts of stress generated by the two major aspects of our lives, can you see how quickly it can all mount up?

Random and short-lived situations of stress are not our real enemies but constant exposure to stress catalysts and the subsequent CUMULATIVE effects of stress *are*. This aspect of stress has been studied in great depth and the following activity has been adapted (for our purposes) from the Holmes and Rahe Life Events Scale and the Life Events Chart by Cary and Rachel Cooper, to draw your attention to the effects of cumulative stress on *your* well-being.

♦ **ACTIVITY 4.4** ♦♦♦

Put a tick in the *Yes* column if you have experienced any of the following events IN THE LAST 12 MONTHS. Then put a circle around the score that best reflects the *impact* that this event had on you at the time.

1...A very small impact   10...A severe impact

Event	Yes	Score
Bought house		1 2 3 4 5 6 7 8 9 10
Sold house		1 2 3 4 5 6 7 8 9 10
Moved house		1 2 3 4 5 6 7 8 9 10
Major house renovation		1 2 3 4 5 6 7 8 9 10
Separated from loved one		1 2 3 4 5 6 7 8 9 10
End of relationship		1 2 3 4 5 6 7 8 9 10
Got engaged		1 2 3 4 5 6 7 8 9 10
Got married		1 2 3 4 5 6 7 8 9 10
Marital problem		1 2 3 4 5 6 7 8 9 10
Awaiting divorce		1 2 3 4 5 6 7 8 9 10
Divorce		1 2 3 4 5 6 7 8 9 10
Child started school/nursery		1 2 3 4 5 6 7 8 9 10
Increased nursing responsibilities for elderly or sick person		1 2 3 4 5 6 7 8 9 10
Problems with relatives		1 2 3 4 5 6 7 8 9 10
Problems with friends/neighbours		1 2 3 4 5 6 7 8 9 10
Pet-related problems		1 2 3 4 5 6 7 8 9 10
Work-related problems		1 2 3 4 5 6 7 8 9 10
Change in nature of work		1 2 3 4 5 6 7 8 9 10
Threat of redundancy		1 2 3 4 5 6 7 8 9 10
Changed job		1 2 3 4 5 6 7 8 9 10
Made redundant		1 2 3 4 5 6 7 8 9 10
Unemployed		1 2 3 4 5 6 7 8 9 10
Retired		1 2 3 4 5 6 7 8 9 10
Increased or new bank loan/mortgage		1 2 3 4 5 6 7 8 9 10
Financial difficulty		1 2 3 4 5 6 7 8 9 10
Insurance problem		1 2 3 4 5 6 7 8 9 10
Legal problem		1 2 3 4 5 6 7 8 9 10
Emotional or physical illness of close family or relative		1 2 3 4 5 6 7 8 9 10

Serious illness of close family or relative requiring hospitalisation		1 2 3 4 5 6 7 8 9 10
Surgical operation experienced by family member or relative		1 2 3 4 5 6 7 8 9 10
Death of partner		1 2 3 4 5 6 7 8 9 10
Death of family member or relative		1 2 3 4 5 6 7 8 9 10
Death of close friend		1 2 3 4 5 6 7 8 9 10
Death of pet		1 2 3 4 5 6 7 8 9 10
Emotional or physical illness of yourself		1 2 3 4 5 6 7 8 9 10
Serious illness requiring your own hospitalisation		1 2 3 4 5 6 7 8 9 10
Surgical operation on yourself		1 2 3 4 5 6 7 8 9 10
Pregnancy		1 2 3 4 5 6 7 8 9 10
Birth of baby		1 2 3 4 5 6 7 8 9 10
Birth of grandchild		1 2 3 4 5 6 7 8 9 10
Family member left home		1 2 3 4 5 6 7 8 9 10
Difficult relationship with children		1 2 3 4 5 6 7 8 9 10
Difficult relationship with parents		1 2 3 4 5 6 7 8 9 10

What is your total score?

Analysis of score:

1–25	26–50	51–75	75–100
Low	Moderate	Medium	High

Obviously, the higher your score over a 12 month period, the more you are prone to a physical, mental, emotional and behavioural reaction. And the impact of an event doesn't cease at the end of the year. It can carry over into the next year to be added to more changes and adaptations in your life, whether pleasant or unpleasant.

When things in our lives change, we have to adapt and this takes physical, mental and emotional energy (*resources*). A bit like draining a well. Say you drain your well by adapting to *pleasant* things, the well runs dry and then an *unpleasant* situation develops. You've little left to cope with it positively.

In terms of *managing stress*:

✤ You should ACKNOWLEDGE that you cannot perceive your 'stress' only in the context of work. *Every* aspect of your life contributes to the cumulative effects of unhealthy stress.

✤ You should look back on your recent past and APPRECIATE the impact that life events have had on you and DECIDE whether you need a respite to replenish spent resources.

✤ You should be prepared to PLAN your year ahead (and adapt your original plans if necessary) based on your ongoing scores.

I've asked you to look at your work and your home, and finally I must ask you to look at YOURSELF. You see, the type of person we are, the relationships we form with other people and the way we *perceive* ourselves and the world about us, all influence the amount of stress we experience.

✤ We all boil at different temperatures ✤

When *that* was said to me, they were introducing me to the Type A and Type B theory. Based on extensive research into the close correlation between personality, behaviour and stress-related illness, it shows how we can so often create our own stress with no help from anyone or anything else.

◆ ACTIVITY 4.5 ◆◆◆

Circle one number between the two extreme statements on each line that best describes how you behave in everyday situations. Bear in mind that scores of 10 or 0 are very extreme and suggest that you *always* do this. If the scores would be different for work and home, complete the questions for work first, then home. If you are *very* brave, conduct this activity in the following way:

1. Complete the activity according to how *you* think you are at work.

2. Complete the activity according to how *you* think you are at home.

3. Ask someone at work to complete the activity according to how they perceive *you* in the workplace.

4. Ask someone at home to complete the activity according to how they perceive *you* at home.

5. Compare all answers and discuss the reasons for the differences.

Behaviour	Score	Behaviour
Intense drive and ambition	10 9 8 7 6 5 4 3 2 1 0	Preference for security and stability
Impatient	10 9 8 7 6 5 4 3 2 1 0	Patient
Often hostile in manner	10 9 8 7 6 5 4 3 2 1 0	Easy-going
Competitive	10 9 8 7 6 5 4 3 2 1 0	Not concerned about winning
Avoiding competition if not confident about success	10 9 8 7 6 5 4 3 2 1 0	Participating for the joy of taking part
Restless	10 9 8 7 6 5 4 3 2 1 0	Finding relaxation easy
Impatient about life	10 9 8 7 6 5 4 3 2 1 0	Taking life as it comes
Quick actioned: in walking, talking, eating and doing	10 9 8 7 6 5 4 3 2 1 0	Relaxed in actions and speech
A stickler for setting and meeting deadlines	10 9 8 7 6 5 4 3 2 1 0	Not driven by the clock
Few hobbies and interests outside work	10 9 8 7 6 5 4 3 2 1 0	Many hobbies and interests
Driven by the need to be the best	10 9 8 7 6 5 4 3 2 1 0	Accepting of personal deficiencies
Fearing failure	10 9 8 7 6 5 4 3 2 1 0	A 'That's life' attitude
Stubborn	10 9 8 7 6 5 4 3 2 1 0	Flexible
Inconsistent in behaviour	10 9 8 7 6 5 4 3 2 1 0	Consistent in behaviour
Slow to seek help	10 9 8 7 6 5 4 3 2 1 0	Willing to seek help
Perceiving the need for help as an admittance of weakness	10 9 8 7 6 5 4 3 2 1 0	Perceiving seeking help as a sign of strength
Bearing grudges	10 9 8 7 6 5 4 3 2 1 0	Never bearing grudges
Not able to delegate	10 9 8 7 6 5 4 3 2 1 0	Able to delegate whenever possible
Not easily trusting	10 9 8 7 6 5 4 3 2 1 0	Trusting
Seeking change	10 9 8 7 6 5 4 3 2 1 0	Preferring the 'old ways'

Self-admonishing	10 9 8 7 6 5 4 3 2 1 0	Self-forgiving
Always rushing	10 9 8 7 6 5 4 3 2 1 0	Never rushing
Often interrupting people	10 9 8 7 6 5 4 3 2 1 0	A good listener
Always hiding feelings	10 9 8 7 6 5 4 3 2 1 0	Always expressing feelings
Eager	10 9 8 7 6 5 4 3 2 1 0	Casual
A 'doer', often without thinking	10 9 8 7 6 5 4 3 2 1 0	A 'thinker' often without action

Your total score:

You are considered to be a Type A if you score over 125.

You are considered to be a Type B if you score less than 125.

Type As are acknowledged to be more prone to stress-related illness. *Very high* scoring As are the real dummies. I daren't tell you what *my* score was! I was made to answer some questions so I'll put them to you:

Why do you think Type As are making themselves more prone to stress-related illness? Look at what the left-hand column is saying about the person.

In which factors from the list should you be aiming to reduce your score?

Before leaving this unit, check that you are fully aware of the negative emotions and feelings you experience at work and at home and the catalysts that provoke them. Be sure that you have thought how you can try to change them into positive emotions. Have you decided which aspects of your behaviour to work on to reduce self-induced negative stress?

UNIT 5

Coping Devices

I'm going to teach you how to become a qualified stress-buster!!

Long ago, some prize joker gave me a book on stress management for my birthday. Inside, he had written, 'Read this and you might enjoy another birthday.'

I hope *you* haven't cheated by turning straight to this section on Coping Devices, as I did. It won't work! I proved it!

Like everything else, the whole issue of COPING DEVICES was made very clear to me once I arrived here. Look what I was shown:

Coping Devices

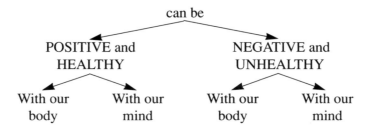

I suppose you've guessed which route *I* took! In my life analysis, I was told that, although I could have *avoided* much of my stress and certainly *dealt* with it better, one of my main problems was that I selected the wrong devices to *cope* with it all. How do you cope with stress?

◆ ACTIVITY 5.1 ◆◆◆

Answer the following questions, collecting perceptions (of you) from other people as much as possible.

1. How do you cope when you are under stress at work?

2. What aspects of (1) do you think are positive and healthy for you?

3. What aspects of (1) do you think are negative and unhealthy for you?

4. How do your coping devices at work affect other people?

    Positively

    Negatively

5. How do you cope when you are under stress at home?

6. What aspects of (5) do you think are positive and healthy for you?

7. What aspects of (5) do you think are negative and unhealthy for you?

8. How do your coping devices at home affect other people?

    Positively

    Negatively

9. What should you do MORE of?

10. What should you do LESS of?

Oh, if I could do it all again!

I'd be A POSITIVE THINKER!

I'd take lots of EXERCISE!

I'd have a BALANCED DIET!

I'd enjoy my HOBBIES!

I'd leave work problems AT WORK!

I'd get my PRIORITIES RIGHT!

I'd AVOID IT so often because I would *plan* and *prepare* and be *organised*!

I'd DEAL with it as it happened because I would put everything into *perspective* and take *control* of myself and my life.

I'd look after MY MIND and I would look after MY BODY! As you must do.

Positive Coping Devices (PCDs) lie at the heart (literally!) of an effective stress management policy. We have a joke here – *a PCD a day keeps the undertaker away!* So why don't we use positive coping devices all the time? Because we're human. Well, *you* are. Unfortunately, humans have the uncanny knack of adopting negative and unhealthy ways of coping with stress because they are *easy* and give immediate relief. Take this chap who came in last week. Let me show you the *S.C.C.* (*S*ituation, *C*oping Device, *C*onsequences) of his life analysis:

Situation	Coping Device	Consequences
Sunday night, dreading Monday	Drank heavily	Damage to liver Hang-over on Monday Everything went wrong
Lousy day Thursday	Picked argument with family at night	More stress in the home No enjoyment of home life Felt worse on Friday

Now, this man, like me, was using negative and unhealthy coping devices with his BODY and his MIND. We usually use a combination. I sought conflict to ease my own tension, moaned and groaned to seek sympathy, punished students when I was really wanting to punish myself, blamed everyone and everything for *my* deficiencies, rejected help because I wanted to wallow in self-pity, forsook hobbies and interests, spurned laughter and humour, drank to obliterate the depression, sank into the settee, ate for comfort, smoked for comfort. . .oh, the list goes on and on. And I used every excuse in the book to justify my reasons for doing so!

Coping Devices: your body

In previous sections, I've drawn your attention to how stress takes its toll on your body because of the constant impact of the STRESS RESPONSE. The 'wear and tear' created by the cumulative effects of this response can do so much damage, can't it? Coping devices pertaining to your BODY are therefore designed to dilute the effects of this persistent barrage on your physical well-being and to make you fitter for the times you have to endure unavoidable stress. There are seven key areas for you to consider here:

- ✤ Diet
- ✤ Exercise
- ✤ Smoking
- ✤ Alcohol
- ✤ Sleep
- ✤ Drugs
- ✤ Body maintenance assistance

First, we'll measure how well you are doing NOW, and then we'll decide on what you are going to do to IMPROVE this aspect of coping.

◆  **ACTIVITY 5.2** ◆◆◆

For the seven aspects of stress management through your body listed below, answer the questions.

Diet

What aspects of your overall diet (food) do you think are healthy and aid the maintenance of a healthy body?
What aspects of your overall diet (food) do you think are unhealthy and detract from the maintenance of a healthy body?

Exercise

What aspects of your overall exercise programme help you in the maintenance of a healthy body?
What aspects of your overall exercise programme detract from the maintenance of a healthy body?

Smoking

> I smoke and it causes the following problems for me:

Alcohol

> The POSITIVE side to my drinking is:

> The NEGATIVE side to my drinking is:

Sleep

> I take the importance of sleep seriously because:

> I experience sleep disturbances because:

Drugs

I use 'hard' drugs, 'soft' drugs, medicines or tablets from my doctor frequently because:

I avoid any form of 'hard' drugs, 'soft' drugs, medicine or tablets from my doctor because:

Body maintenance assistance

I utilise the assistance of professionals to help me maintain the well-being of my body: (Please tick)

Massage/Osteopath/Chiropractic ☐

Alternative medicine practitioner, e.g. Homeopath, Reflexologist, Aromatherapist ☐

Well man/well woman clinics for regular check-ups or annual 'M.O.T.s' ☐

Regular visits to clinics for hair, nails, skin, feet, etc. ☐

They're all important, you know! Your body is taking a lot of stick because of your stressful job, your stressful home and your stressful SELF.

You need to look after it, pamper it, see to its every need because it is the only one you get!

Have you realised that you should be making improvements?

◆ ACTIVITY 5.3 ◆◆◆

Select areas where you think you need help. Tick items in the seven categories studied below that you will try in order to make improvements.

Diet

I will record my total food intake (itemised) every day for one week. At the end of the week I will analyse how balanced it is.	
I will record when, and why, I eat sweet foods and snacks every day for one week. I will acknowledge this as 'comfort eating' and substitute *healthier* snacks at least 50% of the time.	
I will eat less fatty foods and more fruit and vegetables.	
I will grill more foods rather than fry them.	
I will cut down on salt as this is bad for my blood pressure.	
I will reduce the use of sugar in drinks.	
I will reduce my intake of caffeine. I will substitute at least 25% of my intake of tea and coffee with hot water or herbal/lemon teas.	
I will eat more fish and white meat rather than red meat.	
I will drink eight glasses of water per day to improve my digestion.	
I will discuss issues of diet with my family, as it is a vital lifestyle issue.	
What action plans are you making for the future to improve this aspect of body maintenance?	
Where/from whom can you receive help and support in this area?	

Exercise

I *know* that I take insufficient exercise and I am *determined* to rectify this situation.	
I have enjoyed activities in my past but have let them slip because of pressure of work, age, lack of fitness, etc. I will re-establish these links.	
Once I get home, I don't want to go out again. I could arrange regular exercise after work and before I get home.	
I find it difficult to motivate myself to exercise. I could make arrangements with other people and hence be less likely to drop out, as it would mean letting them down.	
I am very unfit and accept that I must build up my fitness slowly.	
I am not very sporty. I could embark on brisk walks because this is just as good for me as jogging, etc.	
I need not go outside for regular exercise. I could design a fitness programme in my home by investing in an exercise bike, etc.	
I can exercise more at work by using stairs instead of lifts, walking to see someone instead of phoning, taking a walk at breaks and lunchtimes, etc.	
I will mow the lawn at home instead of flopping on the settee. I will use *exercise* as a way of *giving* me energy rather than seeing it as a *drain* on my energy.	
What action plans are you making for the future to improve this aspect of body maintenance?	
Where/from whom can you receive help and support in this area?	

Smoking

I am determined to stop smoking because I *know* I would feel better, look better, smell better, be better in my job.	
I will set a date within the next two weeks to give up. I will tell everyone that I am going to give up and ask them for their support.	
I will take advantage of devices available for helping me to give up, e.g. nicotine patches, chewing gums and tablets, hypnosis, acupuncture.	
When I no longer smoke, I will continue to 'spend' cigarette money on a daily basis by placing it in a 'Well done' kitty for one month. I will donate this to a charity and experience a double-edged reward. I will then treat myself to a personal reward, e.g. a piece of furniture for the home, an expensive outfit or some other personal reward that I can look at and say, 'I deserved that!'	
I intend to give up but feel that my life is too stressful at the moment to remove my 'prop'. Yet I want to do *something* positive. I will therefore aim to *give up slowly* and *by degrees*. I will record, on paper, the number of cigarettes I smoke, and when, every day for a week. I will make these charts visible. Each week, I will target a lower daily figure: e.g. Week 1, 40 per day Week 2, 35 per day (Reduce by five each week if the total is high, and two each week if total is fairly low. Never 'borrow' from the next day. Instead, look forward to the next 'legal' cigarette. And never use 'spares' from previous days!)	
What action plans are you making for the future to improve this aspect of body maintenance?	
Where/from whom can you receive help and support in this area?	

Alcohol

I *know* I drink more alcohol than is accepted as good for me. I am determined to address this situation.	
My favourite alcoholic drink is WINE. I will restrict my intake to 14 glasses per week.	
My favourite alcoholic drink is SPIRITS. I will restrict my intake to 14 single measures per week.	
My favourite alcoholic drink is BEER/LAGER. I will restrict my intake to 7 litres per week.	
I will discuss the issue of alcohol intake with my family.	
My excessive drinking causes problems in my home. I am determined to rectify this problem.	
My excessive drinking causes problems at work. I am determined to rectify this problem.	
I need further help with my excessive drinking and will talk to my doctor about it.	
What action plans are you making for the future to improve this aspect of body maintenance?	
Where/from whom can you receive help and support in this area?	

Sleep

I respect sleep as an important part of my stress management devices and acknowledge that *quality* of sleep is more important than *quantity*.	

I have a bed that is big enough/comfortable enough for me and my partner.	
I do not 'clock watch'. If I cannot sleep, I get up. I read, listen to music, talk, etc. to ensure that I am ready to sleep.	
I encourage sleep by making myself tired before retiring.	
I avoid coffee and food near to bedtime, because this activates my digestive system and will keep me awake.	
I never embark on work activities immediately before retiring. I embark on relaxing activities to switch off the stresses of the day.	
I have learned and mastered some relaxation techniques that will help me to switch off my too active mind.	
What action plans are you making for the future to improve this aspect of body maintenance?	
Where/from whom can you receive help and support in this area?	

Drugs

'Hard' drugs destroy my mind as well as my body and I will seek professional help because I do not want to become a drug addict.	
'Soft' drugs are very useful in alleviating my stress but may soon require movement towards hard drugs for the same effect. I must seek professional help to avoid this crisis.	
I am becoming dependent on medicines and tablets from my doctor for what I now know are stress-related ailments. I must talk to my doctor about my *stress* rather than my *ailments*.	

I must aim to *reduce* the amount of drugs and chemicals that I place in my bloodstream by talking to my doctor about stress and my constant visits to him/her for alleviation of my stress-related illnesses.
(Please note: under NO circumstances should you refrain from medical treatment without discussing it first with your doctor!)

What action plans are you making for the future to improve this aspect of body maintenance?

Where/from whom can you receive help and support in this area?

Body maintenance assistance

I have an annual, physical check-up, like an M.O.T. This keeps me and my doctor aware of my general, physical health and highlights problems at an early stage.

I attend the well man/well woman clinic regularly to test for early warning signs of physical problems so that they are easy to put right.

I have a regular massage from a qualified masseur or remedial therapist to help rid my bloodstream and muscles of the toxins created by the stress response.

I pamper myself with regular treatments from qualified people to help me relax, e.g. aromatherapy, reflexology, shen, shiatsu, osteopathy, hypnotherapy.

I am prepared to spend time, effort and money, if necessary, in the pursuit of the healthy maintenance of my body.

> What action plans are you making for the future to improve this aspect of body maintenance?
>
> ---
>
> Where/from whom can you receive help and support in this area?
>
> ---
>
> Looking back through all seven key areas, select five things that you are going to do, starting today.
>
> 1.
>
> 2.
>
> 3.
>
> 4.
>
> 5.

Developing positive coping devices for our bodies is indeed essential to our overall, long-term well-being, because they help to combat the cumulative, unhealthy build-up of stress chemicals that are toxic in nature and ultimately lead to acute stress-related illness.

But the things we do wrong with OUR BODIES are seen, here, in context with what we do wrong with OUR MINDS. Let me explain:

I must tell you about a game we play here. It's called: 'People-watching'. We spot who's about to join us and *why*.

Newcomers are eager to play because they think the game is easy: 'Just look for the ones who do badly in *Activity 5.4* and you can predict who will join us soon.'

◆ **ACTIVITY 5.4** ◆◆◆

Who do you think will join us soon?
Give the reasons for your selection.

It should be David and Peter, right?

They are the ones that the newcomers spotted because they were using negative coping devices and Mark was using positive ones.

But the newcomers were wrong and we knew it. We know it's not always as obvious as that and we've learned to consider the role that the MIND plays in stress management as well as the BODY.

So what happened? Who joined us?

Mark	√

David	√

Peter	×

Why: Body √
      Mind ×

Why: Body ×
      Mind ×

Why: Body ×
      Mind √

Mark's excellent attention to his body was not enough. He persistently used negative coping devices with his mind and his subsequent behaviour created more and more stress at home and at work, his exercising and diet became obsessional and he was a very unhappy man.

David had been a lost cause for ages because he applied negative coping devices physically and mentally.

Peter would be wise to address his physical neglect, but he applies excellent coping devices with his mind and this will keep him away from us for a while longer.

None of us spotted Matthew, the star pupil. He pays as much attention to his mind as he does to his body and will therefore absent himself from here for a very long time.

Coping Devices: your mind

Matthew addresses four main categories, mentally, to cope positively with his stress. Take a look at what he does:

1. INNER DIALOGUE	2. HOME/WORK BOUNDARIES
Purpose: To keep him calm in crisis situations when he realises that he has set up a stress response (or is about to do so), and to switch his negative emotions and feelings to positive ones. He does this to control his stress response that he knows is potentially dangerous to his personal well-being because of its cumulative effects.	*Purpose:* To ensure that work does not invade his home life, social life and hobbies and therefore disrupt his life priorities. Also, to ensure that he is ready for work the next day, physically and mentally refreshed.
3. RELAXATION	4. SUPPORT SYSTEMS
Purpose: To recharge his batteries and keep everything in perspective. Also, as an additional aid to (1) in specific situations.	*Purpose:* To avoid as much stress as possible, to ensure a positive attitude to his life in general, to plan and prepare for stressful times and as a check on the perceptions of other people.

When I arrived here, I was asked to consider what I had done in each category. I remember the shame so vividly! I had been pathetic in these areas. Even the couch potato beat me.

So, I'm going to spell out for you the *purpose* of each of the four categories and then give you as many tips as I can to help you to develop *skills* in each.

1. INNER DIALOGUE

Like you, Matthew knew that he had to find the answers to difficult questions such as:

'How can I stop myself getting angry when I face unpleasant situations?'

'How can I stop worrying about looming deadlines that I cannot meet?'

'How can I stop the resentment I feel when I seem to be working all the time?'

'How can I stop the dread I feel as I drive to work, thinking of the awful day I have ahead of me?'

'How can I stop the frustration I feel on the way home after a bad day at work?'

Remember that the *purpose* of this category is to deal, head on, with your stress response AS IT OCCURS. Inner dialogue (what we say to ourselves, how we reason with ourselves and how we put things into perspective mentally) plays a vital role in changing our perception of the stressful situation.

It's all about *switching off* negative feelings like these:

and *switching on* positive feelings like these:

◆ ACTIVITY 5.5 ◆◆◆

Each of the following ideas has been used to great effect. Read each idea and rate its usefulness (for you) by placing a circle around the appropriate score. Use the following scoring guideline.

3...Very useful, I will definitely use this device
2...Quite useful, I will consider the development of this device
1...Not useful, I, personally, would find this device difficult to learn and use and therefore will not be developing this skill.

Stay calm

Repeat to yourself, 'Calm down, calm down.' At the same time, make a conscious effort to relax your muscles, especially those around your eyes and mouth.	3 2 1
Count backwards from 10 to 1, telling yourself that at each number, you will be calmer and more relaxed.	3 2 1
Ask yourself, 'Why am I getting so het up? Do I enjoy feeling like this? I'd feel better if I remained calm and in control.'	3 2 1
Breathe in deeply and say to yourself, 'Peace and calm in.' Breathe out deeply and say to yourself, 'Problem and tension gone.'	3 2 1
Say to yourself, 'People who lose their cool look stupid and regret it afterwards. I'm not going to do that, I have my pride to think about.'	3 2 1

Say to yourself, 'This is my job. Dealing with this situation effectively is what I am paid to do. I must do the *right thing* rather than what I would *like* to do. So, stay calm, and DO IT WELL.'	3 2 1

Reason with yourself

Tell yourself that this is not the life crisis you are making it out to be. It's temporary and it's minor compared to what *could* happen.	3 2 1
Imagine that you have 100 stress responses left. Ask yourself if this person, this situation, this emotion is worth using one up.	3 2 1
Remember that the person who *really* suffers when you feel a negative emotion is YOU. Ask yourself, 'Am I going to let this person or situation cause ME harm?'	3 2 1
Look at the person/people causing your negative feeling. Ask yourself, 'Who's got the problem? Me, or him/her/them? Why should I pay for *their* behavioural problem?'	3 2 1
Change your anger to compassion or gratitude by saying to yourself, 'Thank goodness I'm not like him/her/them. It must be *awful* to be like them.'	3 2 1
Be tough on yourself. Tell yourself to snap out of this feeling. It's doing you harm and you're almost guaranteeing that you'll handle the situation badly because you are not in full control.	3 2 1
Take pride in your ability to stay in control of your own mind. Move your concentration *away* from your own feelings and *on to* the person or situation. Look for *reasons* by asking yourself, 'WHY is he/she/them acting this way? WHY is this happening?' 'Home in' on *their* stress, not *yours*. Concentrate on *solving* the problem rather than *continuing* it.	3 2 1
Say to yourself, 'Life's short and I'll be a long time dead. Do I want to spend my life feeling like this?'	3 2 1
Say to yourself, 'The life I'm living now is not a rehearsal. This is it! So, make the most of it. Do it right and don't let these hiccups detract me from what are the priorities in my life.'	3 2 1

Remove yourself mentally

Mentally step outside a circle, leaving the problem and the people inside. Look at it all from a distance and look at your own participation in it. Ask yourself, 'Am I handling it well? How do I look? What must they think of me? Do I like/respect ME?'	3 2 1
When a problem is worrying you, but you are unable to solve it *now*, mentally place the problem in a box. Close the lid and walk away. Promise yourself that you will return to this problem as and when you can *do* something about it.	3 2 1
Create a mental 'worry room'. Place all worries in this room and set aside some time in your day to 'visit' this room and see what you can do about any of them. Your visit must be short and very positive.	3 2 1
Give your mind a brief respite from the problem by focusing it on the nicer parts of your life. Ask yourself, 'What am I going to do tonight/this weekend? What colour wallpaper are we going to look for? What preparations do I need to make for the dinner party/decorating/shopping/gardening, etc.?'	3 2 1
Visualise a place where you would love to be. Imagine yourself there, and experience the enjoyment. Ask yourself, 'What would I do? What would I feel? How would I rate the situation I'm in now?'	3 2 1
Mentally 'visit' someone else: a family member, friend or colleague. What are they doing now?	3 2 1
Imagine yourself as an actor in a play. Ask yourself, 'How would X (a famous actor), play this part?'	3 2 1

Use humour

Talk seriously but wear a grin. Say, 'If you don't stop doing that, I'll pull your ears off.'	3 2 1
Say to yourself, 'Oh, beam me up Scottie, *please!*'	3 2 1
Say to yourself, 'I could have been a brain surgeon/a diplomat in the Seychelles. Why did I choose *this* job?'	3 2 1

Revert to childish behaviour because it is 'naughty but nice'. Pull faces, make silly noises, etc. But make sure there are no witnesses.	3 2 1
Imagine something ridiculous happening to the person/room/desk/object/building that is causing you a problem, e.g. blowing up, turning a different colour, disappearing into the floor. (N.B. This device was used to great effect in the television series 'The Fall and Rise of Reginald Perrin' starring Leonard Rossiter.)	3 2 1

Take action

When you realise that you are losing control of your feelings, move the problem to a later time. Suggest, to the other person, that you both 'take a break' and resume the conversation later. Meanwhile, use the time to calm down and prepare yourself to stay *calm* and handle the situation effectively.	3 2 1
Feign pain when you think an injection of humour might relieve the increasing tension. Appear to be deeply hurt and cut to the quick by a remark or someone's behaviour. Hold your hand to your brow and say, 'Susan/Barry/Mr X, I'm devastated by that remark!'	3 2 1
Be assertive when you think humour will not be received well. Say, 'Mr X, I do appreciate/understand/sympathise with how you are feeling/must feel/why you are doing this. However, it's not solving the problem. Can we talk about this/discuss this/sort this out and *solve* the problem that obviously exists?'	3 2 1
Before you say or do anything, picture two words in your mind and decide which one is the best choice for managing your stress positively and healthily: 1. REACT – This is spontaneous and involves no rational prior thought or concern for consequences and outcomes. It is a typical and widely used negative coping device because it vents our tension and makes us feel better in the short term. 2. RESPOND – This asks you to pause for thought: to engage brain before putting mouth into action. Ask yourself, 'What do I want the outcome to be here? What do I want to achieve here? What *should* I say/do? Never mind what I *want* to say/do. What must I say/do to solve the problem?'	3 2 1

Take your worries for a walk. Walking (exercise and hence the removal of stress chemicals from your body), fresh air and a change of scenery will help you to cope with the problem/s on your mind. This can be done at home *and* at work, if only for five minutes.	3 2 1
Use the D/S/W technique. This has been widely used in the field of psychology and involves three personal requests: 1. DETERMINATION – Let me have the determination to work towards changing the things that are wrong and that *can* be changed for the better with effort. 2. SERENITY – Let me have the serenity to accept those things that are wrong but *cannot* be changed, no matter how hard I might try. 3. WISDOM – Let me have the wisdom to know the difference between the two.	3 2 1
Consider the Perfection/Excellence technique. PERFECTION is so rarely achievable. There is always *something* that could be improved upon: doing it better, more neatly, more quickly, with less waste, etc. Those who strive for perfection are therefore constantly in a 'failure' situation and this causes further stress. Ask yourself, 'Why struggle for PERFECTION, when EXCELLENCE will do?'	3 2 1
Never get locked into disagreements. They have a tendency to spiral and draw you in to logical arguments totally unrelated to the problem at hand. We get side-tracked on to other topics, drawn down back alleys and taken off on tangents. Say to yourself, and the other person, 'That's fair comment. However, it's not the *issue* here/Let's get back to the real issue here which is.../Don't let's lose sight of the real issue here which is...'	3 2 1
A Hindu remedy for dwelling, worry, grief and other similar feelings is to accept them as 'Karma' – a little bit like 'That's Life' but deeper. Say to yourself. 'Can I alter what has happened? Can I put the clock back? What's the point of feeling like this?' Say to yourself, 'I must *accept* it because I cannot *change* it.'	3 2 1

| When you begin to feel a negative emotion, imagine it as a monster creeping up on you, determined to do you harm. Say to yourself, 'Oh no, I'm not joining *you* yet, Trimble! I *know* all about stress and the damage it can cause. But I also know that the inner dialogue I am using now will put you off for a little longer. Go away, Trimble! I have a life to live and enjoy!' | 3 2 1 |

How about putting these INNER DIALOGUE devices into practice? We play this game here: we call it PROBLEM REVISITED. We look back at situations that:

— we know we handled badly; — we are not sure we handled as well as possible.

We then re-enact the situation, using a selection of the devices shown above to create a better outcome.

◆ ACTIVITY 5.6 ◆◆◆

After reading each situation, state which negative feeling you *did* or *would* experience, and then switch it to a more positive feeling using your chosen devices from the previous activity. There is space for you to suggest three situations.

Situation	*Negative feeling*	*Inner dialogue*
A senior manager has lost his temper with you in a meeting, in front of your colleagues.	Upset, hurt, embarrassed, angry	*He* is the one with a problem. He wants to show *me* up, but, by staying in control, I'm going to show *him* up. I'll stay calm and talk to him later today.
You do not see eye to eye with your boss *again*.		
One of your colleagues is absent *again* and you have lost essential free time that you were relying on to work.		

Your day has been fraught with problems. Your mind is dwelling on them during the journey home.		
You will be late for work because your car/bus has a flat tyre.		
You have been asked to make a presentation to the entire staff next week.		
On your journey to work on your worst day, you begin to feel agitated and dread the day ahead.		

Look back over *Activities* 5.5 and 5.6. Record *five* Inner dialogue devices that you feel will be useful and that you will use:

1.

2.

3.

4.	
5.	

2. HOME/WORK BOUNDARIES

Matthew values this category very highly. The devices he uses ensure that the problems of work do not invade and upset his home life. They also ensure that his family and friends do not suffer because of his stressful job.

Me? I used home to:

— finish off bits of work;

— dwell on the problems of my day at work;

— worry about the following day;

— moan and groan about work;

— dump my work-related tension on my family and friends.

Matthew divided the work-home boundary into three areas, A, B and C:

Like Matthew, you must develop coping devices:

— at the very end of your working day (A);

— during your journey home (B);

— as soon as you get home (C).

◆ ACTIVITY 5.7 ◆◆◆

In the left-hand column list the positive and healthy things you do now and in the right-hand column identify things that you don't do now but should try to do in the future.

Now	**In the future**
A. At the end of the working day:	
B. On the journey home:	
C. At home:	

❖

Now let's look at the sort of things you *could* do to help you to make these home/work boundaries more defined.

◆   **ACTIVITY 5.8**   ◆◆◆

Consider the ideas in each of the three areas. Tick any item that you already use or might try in the future.

At the end of the working day

Imagine you have two sets of batteries: one for home and one for work. Think about exchanging them as you move from work to home.	

Imagine you have two overcoats: one for work and one for home. Change overcoats mentally as you leave work and put on your home overcoat.	
Have a 'worry' folder at work containing all the problems that evoke negative emotions. File this folder as you leave work.	
Sit quietly at the end of the working day for five minutes to 'wind down'. Relax and tune yourself in to how you should feel now you are going home.	
At the end of the working part of your day, sit and make your 'To Do' list for tomorrow. Place it in a prominent position for the following day.	
Try leaving your briefcase behind!	
Clear your desk ready for tomorrow and tell yourself that it will be purposeful and rewarding.	
Place 'reminder stickers' on your desk so you know where to start tomorrow.	

On the journey home

Have a tape recorder in the car. As you think about what needs to be done at work the following day/week, record it on the tape.	
Play your favourite tapes in the car on the way home: loud music, relaxing music, comedy programmes to make you laugh.	
Stop on the way home for a coffee, collect your thoughts and switch off.	
Try going shopping or browsing around shops to refocus your mind before you go home.	
Try going swimming (or another activity) before you go home.	
Go for a walk somewhere between work and home to ponder on the day and switch to what you want to do at home.	
Identify a 'landmark' on the journey home. When you reach this marker, discipline yourself to shifting your thoughts to home.	
Meet someone after work for a coffee, a chat or to share some form of exercise.	
Take another route home to see something different.	

At home

Associate the gate and/or door with forgetting work.	
Change your clothes as soon as you get in. Change from work clothes into home clothes and associate this with switching off.	
Have a bath or shower as soon as possible after getting home. Wash away work.	
Sit quietly, have a coffee and read the paper or a book. Enjoy the peace and quiet.	
Take the dog for a walk. No dog? Just go for a walk!	
Allow a 'stress session' early in the evening with your partner or a friend in which you can both off-load the problems you both feel. Do be sure, though, to set a time limit!	
Revel in being able to 'potter' and do things you always intend to get round to doing.	
Use some self-discipline. *Make* yourself do things unconnected with work.	
Make a 'To Do' list for home in the same way as you do for work. Concentrate on achieving things at home.	
Share the cooking, cleaning and general housework. It's a wonderful way of switching off!	
Allocate one evening a week for sharing the shopping. You *have* to switch off from work in this environment!	
Allocate regular times to hobbies (not work-related) and activities that you enjoy throughout the week. Place them in a high priority position.	

3. RELAXATION

In this category, Matthew includes things such as relaxation techniques, hobbies and socialising. He uses them all to recharge his batteries and to help to keep everything in perspective.

I tried a relaxation technique once. Only once; it didn't give me instant results, so I dismissed it as rubbish. I used to have lots of hobbies, but, as my life analysis revealed, they slowly got pushed to one side to make room in my life for work and worrying. The same thing happened to my social life which was probably a good thing for my friends, because I had become a moaning bore anyway.

If I tested you on the level of your skills in relaxation, how well would you do? Do you think it is important?

◆ **ACTIVITY 5.9** ◆◆◆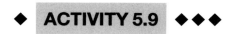

Tick the boxes that reflect your use of, and ability in, the following areas and answer the questions.

Relaxation and tension control techniques

My ability to use relaxation and tension control techniques in the following areas is:	*Good*	*Average*	*Poor*
Releasing my tension on the way home from work			
Relaxing before what I know will be a difficult class			
Relaxing before a difficult meeting			
Relaxing after a difficult class			
Relaxing before a presentation			
Switching off my stress response before going to sleep			

Describe the relaxation and tension control techniques that you use.

> In what situations would you like to be able to use these techniques? Explain why.

Some tried and tested relaxation and tension control techniques are given in the *Appendix* (p. 75). You may find these useful or try some of the many tapes, books and videos that are available. Find what works best for you.

Hobbies

> How important do you think hobbies are as a means of relaxing? Give reasons for your answer.

> What hobbies and activities do you participate in during the evening?

> How many weekday evenings, on average, do you use for these hobbies and activities?

> What hobbies and activities do you participate in at the weekend?

Do you use hobbies and activities for relaxation enough?

What hobbies and activities have you dropped and why?

What improvements can you make in the future?

Socialising

I would describe my attention to the following as:	Good	Average	Poor
The upkeep of friendships			
The maintenance of an active social life			

In an average month, state and describe the amount of socialising you have done.

Are you happy with the amount and quality?

Are your family and friends happy with the amount and quality? (Please check!)

What improvements should you make in the future?

4. SUPPORT SYSTEMS

When I was asked what I thought support systems were, all I could think of was the *hierarchy* at work. You know the sort of thing: 'If you have a problem, talk to your Head of Department.' If *I* took a problem to *my* H.O.D., he saw it as a sign of weakness on my part. I lost two promotions that way!

There's more to support systems than the ones in (or not in) place at work.

We've been taught here to perceive support systems as PEOPLE and PAPER.

I thought I might be able to catch self-sufficient Matthew out in this category, but alas, no. He uses these as much as those in the previous three categories. He's really got this coping with stress mentally off to a fine art. He uses support systems to *avoid* as much stress as possible. He uses them to stay positive and he uses them to plan and prepare for difficult times. We've estimated here that, by using these devices, Matthew avoids 60% of the sort of stress that I would have walked into, time after time after time.

Let's take the issue of getting support from PEOPLE first.

◆ **ACTIVITY 5.10** ◆◆◆

Answer each of the following questions. If your answer is *Yes* tick the appropriate box on the LADDER. For *No*, tick the box on the SNAKE. Record your totals at the end and then answer the questions.

☐ ← I am able to talk to my manager about problems relating to work. → ☐

☐ ← I am able to talk to my manager about problems relating to home. → ☐

☐ ← I am able to talk to colleagues at work about work-related problems. → ☐

☐ ← I am able to talk to certain colleagues at work about home-related problems. → ☐

☐ ← I belong to a 'group' at work that help me to stay positive by its use of humour, banter, rapport and conversation. → ☐

☐ ← I avoid dumping my stress on colleagues at work, i.e. picking arguments, having temper tantrums, etc. → ☐

☐ ← I avoid dumping my stress on my family, i.e. picking arguments, temper tantrums, moods, etc. → ☐

☐ ← I am able to talk to my family about work-related problems, but never allow it to dominate the conversation. → ☐

☐ ← I am able to talk to my friends about work-related problems but never allow it to dominate the conversation. → ☐

☐ ← I am able to talk to my family about home-related problems in a positive, calm and understanding manner. → ☐

☐ ← I have other people in my support system that I can talk to. → ☐

TOTAL: [   ]   TOTAL: [   ]

What do you do well? (Look at the ladder.)

What factors are lacking from your support system? (Look at the snake.)

What improvements can you make in the future?

Now let's look at getting support from PAPER.

Matthew uses these devices regularly, and *not only* when he perceives a problem to be present or imminent. He uses them in order to keep track of what is going on and often to identify minor issues before they become major ones.

To appreciate how and why these paper devices work, we must acknowledge how our minds work. I had always worked *against* my mind instead of *with* it or *for* it.

You see, it all hinges on the fact that, under stress, our minds tend to flit from one thing to another, while retaining the uncanny knack of staying away from what they *should* think about. It's called *denial* here, and is all part of our mind's way of avoiding unpleasant issues or facts.

We BURY these unpleasant issues.

We LOCK AWAY the things that we should confront and solve.

We HIDE from facts that will hurt us.

We REFUSE TO ACCEPT things that contradict the image we want to have of ourselves and our lives.

The best way of addressing these issues and problems, and hence solving them, is to write things down and create an organised picture, as Matthew does.

◆ **ACTIVITY 5.11** ◆◆◆

Read through each of Matthew's two ideas. See how he completed them; how and why he used them to his benefit. Decide how *you* could use them for *your* benefit. Either copy the charts or adapt them and then complete them.

1. Benefit/Drawback

Matthew knows that problems in *one* aspect of his life can be coped with more effectively if *other* aspects are in better shape. So when he identifies in himself that he is feeling worried, angry, frustrated or dwelling heavily on an issue, he uses a simple two-column exercise to write down the benefits and drawbacks of his emotional state.

One of his completed charts is given on p. 70.

2. HOMEWORK BOUNDARIES

Matthew conducts this activity every three months. He keeps past records and compares them all, thus keeping track of what problems he has resolved, what issues are not being attended to, what problems are likely to arise and how much control and responsibility he is actually taking in his life.

Matthew believes that by participating in this activity (and Idea 1), he is taking ownership of his own stress and not allowing himself to abdicate responsibility to someone or something else.

He takes each of the four sources of life stress (home, work, finance, health) in turn and concentrates on one at a time. For each, he draws lines (like the branches of trees) to record any issue that might be bothering him, no matter how small or apparently trivial.

After completing the exercise for all four sources, he sits back and studies the whole picture carefully, adding any afterthoughts. Then he answers some pertinent questions and finally, he talks over his findings with his support system team.

One of his life-tree record sheets is given on pp. 71–72.

Benefits/Drawbacks

How do I feel?

Angry

What is creating this feeling?   Susy (new member of dept.)
Never participates in meetings. No ideas. Has to be told
everything. Poor discipline.

Benefits of this feeling:	Drawbacks to this feeling:
I get sympathy from people when I complain about her. I make my point to her when I show my annoyance.	It takes me away from concentrating on higher priority items. I'm dwelling on it and making myself worse. My stress response is switched on all the time. I'm losing my cool and control – no solutions though.

What can I do to help myself?

Switch off. Come away from it. Stand back.

What can I do to resolve the problem?

List her role. What do I want her to do/be? Discuss it
with her. Work on <u>her</u> problems, not <u>mine</u>.

Who do I need to talk to and what about?

Susy. Her colleagues. Her pastoral head.

How can I prevent this happening again?

Better induction.
Don't leave it so long.
Get involved in adverts and selection for my dept.

Life-tree Record Sheet

Date: **April 1995**

Three-monthly review:

Good: Solved the problem with Yr 12 reports clashing with Parents'
Evening. Changed the stupid car for Margaret.

Bad: Let myself be talked into the working party for School and
Community + the new conservatory.

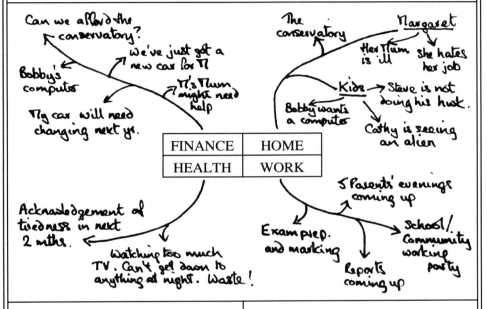

FINANCE	HOME
HEALTH	WORK

Can we afford the conservatory?

We've just got a new car for M

M's Mum might need help

Bobby's computer

My car will need changing next yr.

The conservatory

Margaret

Her Mum is ill · she hates her job

Kids → Steve is not doing his hwk.

Bobby wants a computer

Cathy is seeing an alien

5 Parents' evenings coming up

Acknowledgement of tiredness in next 2 mths.

Watching too much TV. Can't get down to anything at night. Waste!

Exam prep. and marking

Reports coming up

School / Community working party

What are the major problems at home?

Ongoing:
Decision on the conservatory

New development:
Steve is not doing his homework

Predicted:
Conservatory — too much work / worry

What are the major problems at work?

Ongoing:

New development:
Involvement on W. Party

Predicted:
Too much to do end of June

continued

What are the major problems financially?	What are the major problems in my health?
Ongoing: Conservatory	Ongoing: STILL haven't joined the golf club
New development: TI's car TI's Mum	New development: Stomach playing up. Not enough exercise and relaxation
Predicted: Financial overload, esp. cost of conservatory	Predicted: Less time to relax if I don't get organised now

What can I do in each area?

Home: Decide with TI about the conservatory. Look at all the other constraints. Delay for a yr.

Work: Find out how much involvement/time is needed for the W. Party. Start exams/reports etc.

Finance: See the bank and ask their advice

Health: Join the golf club. Keep active at night. A<u>chieve</u> something at home.

Whom do I need to talk to? What help can I find?

Home: TI. TI's Mum. Steve. Cathy

Work: The Francis

Finance: Shop around more for the conservatory. Bank

Health: TI. What does she think?

UNIT

6

Stress Check ▬▬▬▬▬▬▬▬▬▬▬

Now, before you run away and start implementing some of the ideas I have given you, let's make sure that you are completely *organised* in your approach.

◆ ▨▨ **ACTIVITY 6.1** ▨▨ ◆◆◆

Answer the questions by looking back at any relevant sections in the book.

State why you have now got a positive attitude to the stress in your life.
State your main WARNING SIGNS of stress. Physical: Mental and emotional: Behavioural:
What are the CATALYSTS of your stress?

What are the PRIMARY CAUSES of your stress?

What NEGATIVE coping devices are you going to eliminate/reduce:

With your body?

With your mind?

What POSITIVE coping devices are you going to use in the future:

With your body?

With your mind?

Apart from yourself, who will benefit from your improved stress management?

Appendix

THE RELAXATOR TECHNIQUE (designed by the Stress Foundation) includes progressive relaxation, autogenic training and visualisation. Learning the process involves following these guidelines:

✤ Set aside 20 minutes' undisturbed time in a quiet place. (Use a timer.)

✤ Lie on your back with one pillow under your neck and another under your knees. Loosen all tight clothing. Rest your arms at your side, palms up.

✤ Do not TRY to relax, let it come naturally.

✤ Breathe in slowly and gently from your stomach to a count of four.

✤ Breathe out quite forcibly to a count of four. Never over-breathe, as this can cause dizziness. Use regular, comfortable breaths.

✤ As you breathe out, let all your muscles go loose. Imagine yourself as a deflating balloon.

✤ With each out-breath, let a group of muscles go. Start with your shoulders; then your neck; then your arms; then your chest; then your stomach; then your legs; then your face and scalp.

✤ When you have mastered this technique, include a feeling of heaviness in the muscles as you relax them.

✤ Now allow your breathing to be more natural and concentrate on feeling heavy and warm, i.e. as you breathe out, relax a group of muscles *and* feel them warm.

✤ Visualise a peaceful place – a place that you would find soothing and calming.

✤ Do not rush this technique. Take it steadily and feel the relaxation in one area of your body before tackling the next. At the end of your session, stretch and get up slowly. Never rush around after a relaxation session. Enjoy the benefits of it and take the relaxed state away with you.

✤ Once you have mastered the skills, you can use this technique *anywhere* and for a few moments at a time. It does not have to be in a quiet room or when alone.

A QUICK RELEASE OF TENSION. Breathing techniques can be used on their own and can be of benefit in a difficult situation. The emphasis is on controlled breathing. For example:

✤ Take several breaths that are deeper than usual and where the breathing out is quite forceful.

✤ Return to normal breathing for a few seconds.

✤ Repeat the exercise several times.

❖ As you breath in say to yourself, 'Calm in'.
   As you breathe out say to yourself, 'Tension out'.
❖ At the same time, imagine the tension flowing out of your body.

THE CAT EXERCISE. When you have more time, undisturbed, try a technique that has proved useful for centuries:

❖ Sit or lie comfortably.
❖ Tense *all* your muscles for two seconds, including hands, face, arms and legs.
❖ Release them suddenly and *feel* the difference.
❖ Breathe normally for several seconds but hold on to the relaxed feeling.
❖ Now concentrate on the muscles in your face; especially the eyes, mouth and jaw. Make sure they are fully relaxed.
❖ Slowly move down to each group of muscles in your body from head to toes. Relax each group as you 'visualise' them.
❖ Keep going back to check that nothing has tightened up once you have moved on. You will find that they *do* tighten automatically once they think you are 'not looking'. Keep reminding them to relax.
❖ With practice, you can scan the muscles in your entire body to identify which muscles are tensing and not abiding by your rules.
❖ These are the muscles you need to work on throughout the day, e.g. keep checking on them to see how tense they are when driving, in class, doing paperwork, etc. (Facial muscles are notorious for this.)
❖ Once mastered, this technique can be practised very quickly and great benefit can be achieved many times in a day.

SLEEPY SKILLS. If you find it difficult to get to sleep, it is probably because your mind is too active; it has too many things buzzing around to allow it to relax. You have to take control and make it switch off by focusing your mind on something other than anxious thoughts, the re-living of incidents, problems and worries.

❖ Use repetition: something that involves counting and visualising an activity, e.g. visualise yourself doing five or six exercises in a gymnasium (say, ten of each). Each time your mind wanders to its own thoughts, bring it back and start the exercises again from the first one.
❖ Try breathing and relaxation techniques. The only problem with this is that, if you then use them during the day, your mind and body may associate them with sleep. It is better to have relaxation and breathing techniques for your waking hours and *specific* sleepy skills for night. In this way, you train your mind and body to do what *you* want them to do.
❖ Whatever happens, and however long it takes to master these skills, do not panic or worry if you fail. Get up, do something and then try again. Reassure yourself that the sleep you finally get will be good quality and sufficient to see you through the next day.